A NICHT AT THE PICTERS

The Broons clan, Oor Wullie, Fat Bob, Soapy Soutar and Wee Eck all had one thing in common — they'd never miss out on a visit "tae the picters". Maggie and Daphne Broon preferred handsome leading men and lovey-dovey films, of course. Not so Wullie and the menfolk — nothing short of a "guid cartoon an' a rip-roarin' cowser" film would do for them — "an' nae kissin'!" Fortunately, chuckles and thrills were among the few things that weren't rationed back then — so here are some of the films and stars The Broons, Wullie and his pals would have queued to view during The Roaring Forties.

"Ah, Whit Bonny!" Every Mum's favourite, Shirley Temple, who starred in "Young People" made in 1940.

FOR THE LADIES

"The Sword Arm o' The Law" Tyrone Power, who cut a dashing figure and lots of Zs in "The Mark Of Zorro".

"Ye Dinnae Sing Tae Me Like That!" "Bitter Sweet" and "New Moon" both produced in 1940 and both featuring the vocal talents of Jeanette MacDonald and Nelson Eddy.

"Fast-Footed Fred" The production of "Broadway Melody of 1940", starring Fred Astaire, had Daphne wishing to be swept doon the stairs o' 10 Glebe St in her ba'goon.

"Ups-A-Daisy" No chance of feeling down watching Mickey Rooney and Judy Garland in "Strike Up The Band".

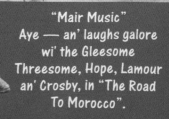

"Mair Music" Aye — an' laughs galore wi' the Gleesome Threesome, Hope, Lamour an' Crosby, in "The Road To Morocco".

"Marx Oot o' Ten . . ."
. . . eleven — for The Marx Brothers and their own brand of bedlam in "Go West".

"Whaur Did Ye Get That Hat?" "The Gold Rush" was directed by and starred Charlie Chaplin 'way back in 1925. He re-edited and narrated it in 1942. There's cold in them thar hills.

FOR THE LADDIES

"Is It A Fecht Ye're Wantin'?" Few were quicker at drawin' fowk intae the picters than Alan Ladd in films like "This Gun For Hire".

"A Pirate Treasure" "The Black Swan" was fu'o'cannons an' cuttlasses an' muskets an', for the bigger laddies, like Joe Broon, there wis Maureen O'Hara.

"Strummin' Strings" The Duke of Uke — that's George Formby in films like "Spare A Copper" and "Turned Out Nice Again" — it always did with our George.

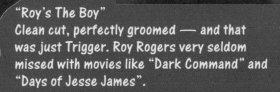

"Roy's The Boy" Clean cut, perfectly groomed — and that was just Trigger. Roy Rogers very seldom missed with movies like "Dark Command" and "Days of Jesse James".

The Sunday Post 16th June 1940

OOR WULLIE 1940-1949

The Sunday Post 14th January 1940

The Sunday Post 28th July 1940

The Sunday Post 8th September 1940

The Sunday Post 15th September 1940

The Sunday Post 27th October 1940

Correction Corner

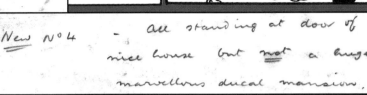

Even the great Dudley D. Watkins didn't always get things right first time. He'd send his interpretation of the script, in pencil, to R. D. Low, the Managing Editor of Children's Publications.

Mr Low would then make any alterations he thought necessary, before returning the job to Dudley, who would complete it in ink.

The particular corrections shown on this page were discovered pencilled on the back of the finished artwork, which was printed in The Sunday Post on October 24th, 1943. Most artist's instructions tended to be erased or destroyed — so this example could well be unique. Pencil roughs were the norm at that time, as artist and scriptwriter didn't always visualise a scene the same way. This system ensured the original concept was followed as closely as possible.

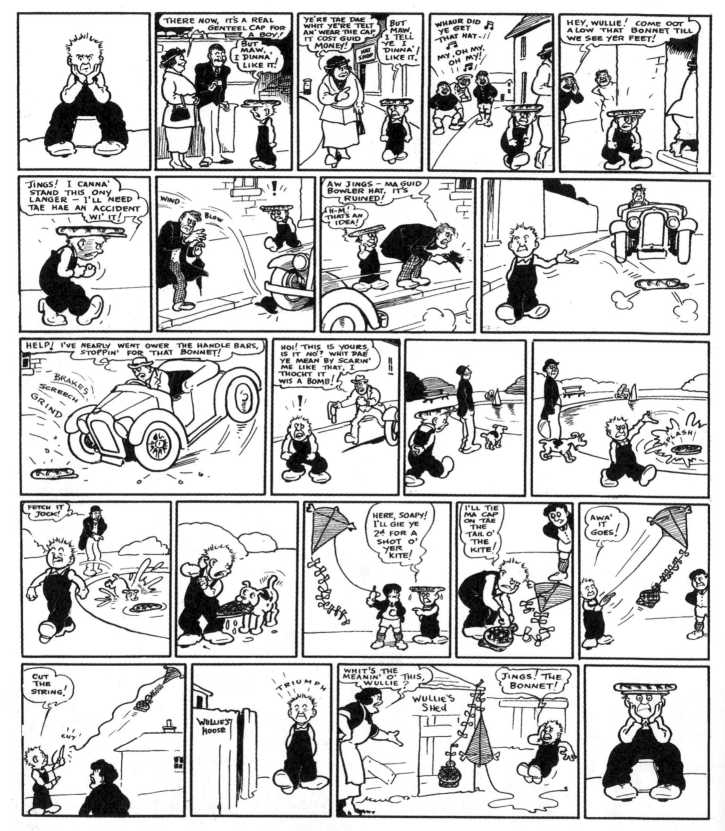

The Sunday Post 3rd November 1940

OOR WULLIE 1940-1949

The Sunday Post 26th January 1941

The Sunday Post 24th November 1940

The Sunday Post 16th February 1941

OOR WULLIE 1940-1949

The Sunday Post 30th March 1941

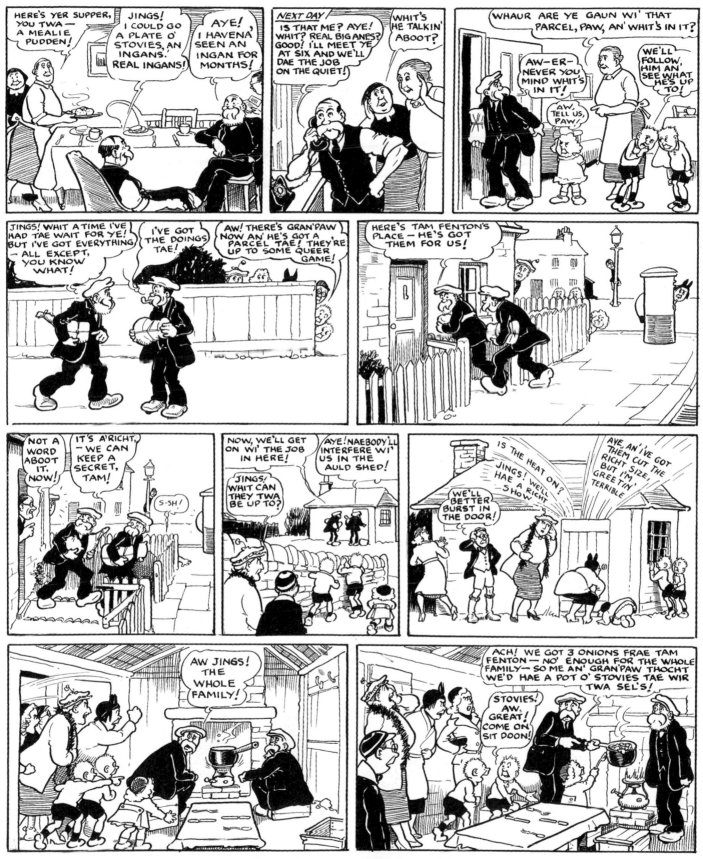

The Sunday Post 23rd February 1941

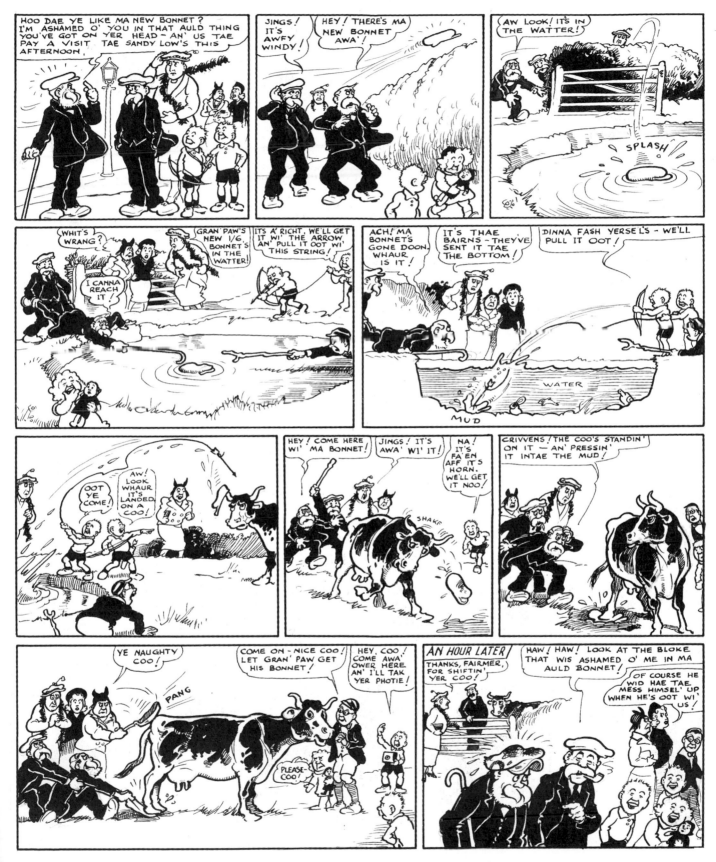

The Sunday Post 27th April 1941

The Sunday Post 21st September 1941

The Sunday Post 18th May 1941

DINNAE MENTION THE WAR

It wasn't all doom and gloom in the early 40s as these headlines and articles show.

GOOD-BYE MR CHIP!

IN Scottish restaurant and street, wherever people meet to eat, they're holding up their hands aghast, and sighing for the glorious past, and muttering with trembling lips, " We can't get any fish and chips!"

The scarcity of cooking fat has brought us—rich and poor—to that!

For the fish and chip man things are bleak — he's closed a couple of days a week.

It's rousing all his patrons' ire, so now the fat is in the fire! This shattering news has rocked the nation, threatening society's foundation.

Just think, if things get any worse, even if you've a bulging purse, and give the man a generous tip, you scarce can buy a tuppeny chip—in tiny poke that's rather tight—to munch in street on Saturday night!

And soon, alas! that pungent smell may vanish from our streets as well.

You Hollywood moguls, here's a tip—a film named " Goodbye, Mr Chip."

But maybe Woolton will hear this plea—and bring my pokie back to me!

PURE WASTE

I HAD twelve bottles of whisky in my cellar, and my wife told me to empty the contents of each and every bottle down the sink—" or else!" So I said I would, and proceeded with the unpleasant task.

I withdrew the cork from the first bottle and poured the contents down the sink, with the exception of one glass, which I drank.

I extracted the cork from the second bottle and did likewise, with the exception of one glass, which I drank.

I then withdrew the cork from the third bottle and emptied the good old booze down the sink, except a glass which I drank.

I pulled the cork from the fourth sink and poured the bottle down the glass, which I drank.

I pulled the bottle from the cork of the next and drank one sink out of it, and poured the rest down the glass.

I pulled the sink out of the next glass and poured the cork down the bottle.

I pulled the next cork out of my throat, poured the sink down the bottle, and drank the glass.

Then I corked the sink with the glass, bottled the drink, and drank the pour.

When I had emptied everything I steadied the house with one hand and counted the bottles and the corks and the glasses with the other, which were twenty-nine.

To be sure, I counted again when they came by, and I had seventy-four, and as the house came by I counted them again, and finally I had all the house and the bottles and the corks and the glasses counted except one house and one bottle, which I drank.

[From " Three Six ", an Observer Corps magazine.]

FOR TOUGH BEARDS

USE tea instead of water when shaving. The lather made by the tea makes tough beards much easier to shave. This is an old Navy custom.—The Captain.

Wasn't His Face Red !

Tom Blower, the Channel swimmer, who is in the navy, tells how when joining up he reported to a depot.

He was ordered to take a swimming test — two lengths of a bath and float for three minutes in a deck suit.

When he had performed the test the instructor nodded his head approvingly and commented, " Not bad, we'll make a swimmer of you yet."

The instructor's face was a study when he later learned that Blower was the man who swam the Channel in 1937!

BACK IN THOSE PRE-WAR DAYS!

COMPARISON of prices now and in grandmother's day in last weeks " Sunday Post " were interesting, but we don't need to go back to the eighties for big changes.

After looking over a housekeeping book from 1934 to 1938, made this comparison :—

	Pre-War.	Now.
Sugar	2½d per lb.	5d per lb.
Butter	1s 2d per lb.	1s 7d per lb.
Cheese	10d to 1s per lb.	1s 7d per lb.
Syrup	4d per lb.	8½d per lb.
Lentils	3d per lb.	6d per lb.
Eggs	10d-1s 4d per doz.	3s 6d
Tea	2s 8d per lb.	3s 6d per lb.
Cooking apples	1s for 3½ lb.	6d per lb.
Beef (stewing)	1s 2d per lb.	1s 6d per lb.
Beef (boiling)	10d per lb.	1s 2d per lb.
Coal	1s 6d per cwt.	2s per cwt.
Tobacco	8½d per oz.	1s 5d per oz.
Chocolates	4d per qtr lb.	1s per qtr lb.

—AND NOT A DROP TO DRINK

I'M afraid 1942 will be launched on a sea of lemonade.

A bottle of " fizz " will be the only Ne'erday bottle for most folk this year.

THERE WAS A RIOT ALL RIGHT

WHEN I plugged in to a call signal on my telephone switchboard near midnight, I heard what I took to be screams, followed by sounds of choking and furniture being knocked over. No voice spoke.

I identified the source of the call as an office which I knew should be locked up for the night.

A message was flashed to the police, and the flying squad soon had a cordon round the building.

* * * *

The telephone had been upset in a contest between the office cat and an intruder of the species!—M. M.

CAUGHT TROUT WHILE DRIVING CAR

A Stirling man caught a 1¼ lb trout under unusual circumstances at Ballantrae.

He was motoring along the banks of the River Stinchar, when the fish fell on the seat beside him.

The trout had slipped from the beak of a seagull flying overhead.

GRILLED SCOTS' DEBT TO DAWSON

By NUMBER ONE
ENGLAND, 2; SCOTLAND, 3.
(Half-time—2-2.)

THERE is such a thing as playing your opponents to a standstill. There is also such a thing as playing yourselves to a standstill. That is what England did at St James's Park, Newcastle.

We shall never know how our boys survived that gruelling, despite the fact that we had Jerry Dawson, who stands supreme in the goalkeeping business.

Holidays?—But Where?

IF you're lucky enough to get a holiday this year, you'll be luckier still if you can find accommodation easily in some Scottish resorts.

Many of them have increased their populations—some by 25 per cent. Chief reason—evacuees. But there IS some room left.

Dunoon and Rothesay—Only accommodation available in houses that let with attendance, boarding-houses, and hotels.

Largs—Still room for at least 10,000 holiday-makers. Brisk bookings.

Millport—Fair number of houses to let for summer, ample accommodation in hotels and boarding-houses.

Gourock and Helensburgh—Tough job finding a bed in either.

Oban—Room for close on 4000 visitors.

Girvan—Despite numerous evacuees, landladies will be able to squeeze in another 2000 people.

Ayr, Prestwick, and Troon — Pretty hopeless for holiday-makers.

Dunbar and N. Berwick—Many large and small houses to let.

North-East Coast—Accommodation very limited.

THE FROZEN LIMIT

ONE night recently a friend of mine put, as usual, his dentures in a tumblerful of water.

In the morning he found his teeth fixed in a permanent grin, firmly encased in ice.

What he said, and how he got them out, are matters for the reader's own imagination.—False, But True.

The Sunday Post 24th August 1941

The Sunday Post 4th January 1942

The Sunday Post 12th October 1941

The Sunday Post 26th October 1941

OOR WULLIE 1940-1949

OOR WULLIE 1940-1949

The Sunday Post 19th April 1942

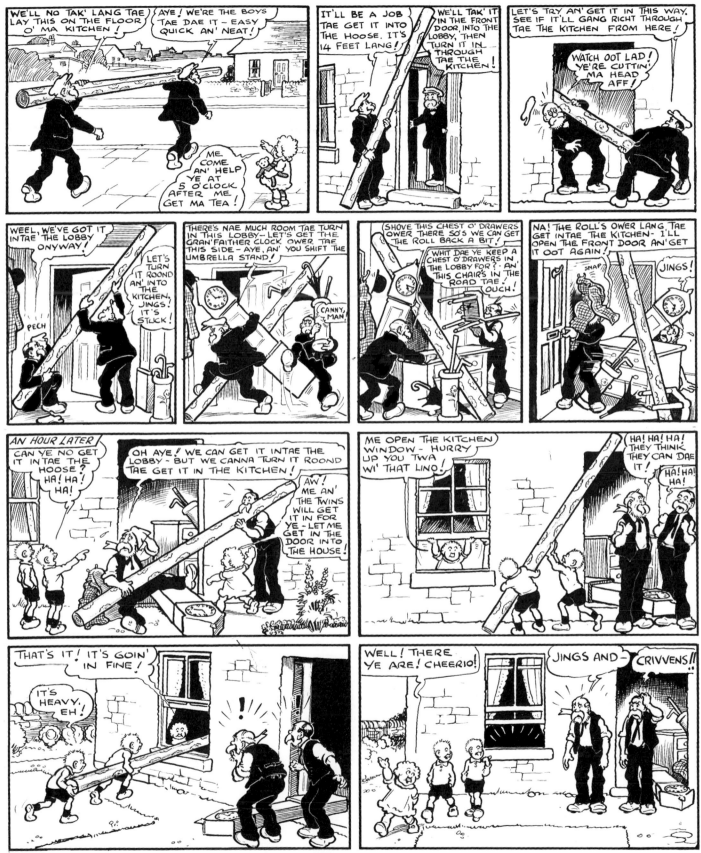

The Sunday Post 3rd May 1942

OOR WULLIE 1940-1949

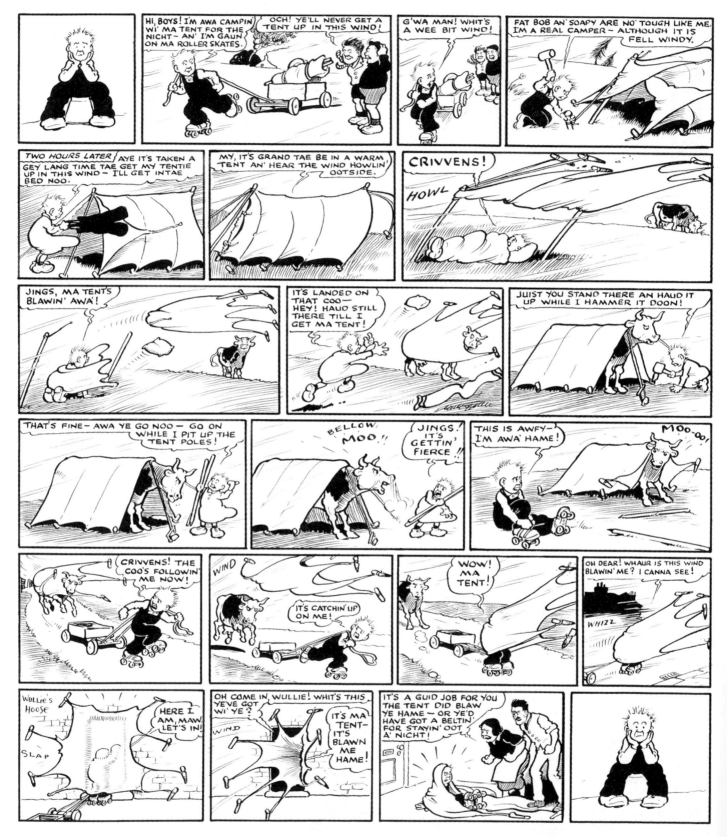

The Sunday Post 9th August 1942

The Sunday Post 18th October 1942

The Sunday Post 30th August 1942

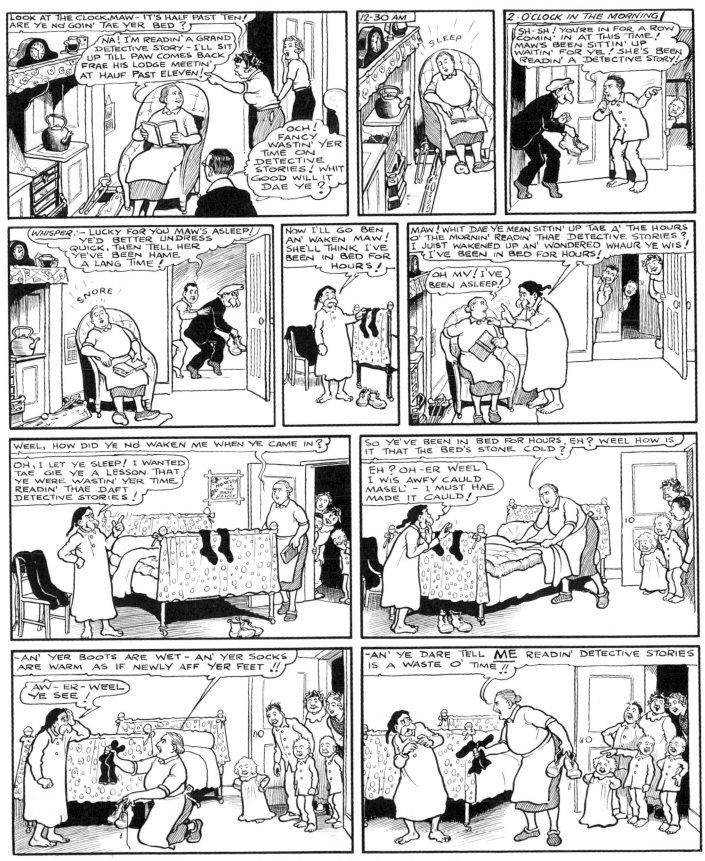

The Sunday Post 29th November 1942

OOR WULLIE 1940-1949

The Sunday Post 3rd January 1943

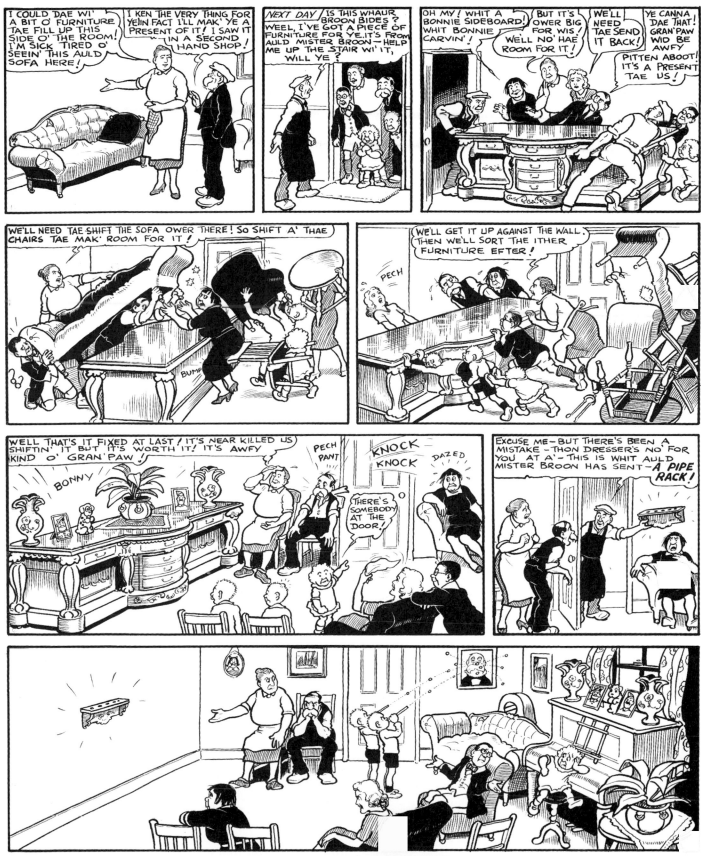

The Sunday Post 6th December 1942

OOR WULLIE 1940-1949

The Sunday Post 20th December 1942

A NICHT AT THE PICTERS

"A Cup O' Tea An' A Cary-On" Cary Grant, star of "Mr Lucky", is another of Daphne's favourites. She thinks he's Archie — Leach, that is — we telt ye Daphne was fickle.

"The Kirrie Krook — er — Crook" Kirriemuir-born David Niven played the gentleman crook, Raffles, in the film of the same name. Daphne says he could pinch her pudden supper onytime — Daphne's fickle.

"Donat Forsake Me, Oh, My Darlin'!" Robert Donat in "Goodbye, Mr Chips". Aye, ye've guessed it — Daphne likes him tae — just hand her "Chips" on a plate.

"Maw! The Colman's Here!" Ronald Colman, that is — in "The Talk Of The Town". Daphne reckons she wid be, if she wis goin' oot wi' him.

FOR THE LADIES

"Crawford Tak's The Biscuit" Joan Crawford starred in "They All Kissed The Bride". Daphne was heard to exclaim "Whit? A' o' them? An' got married tae? It's no' fair!"

"Young Enough For Daphne" Another Robert — Robert Young in "Slightly Dangerous". The only time Daphne's dangerous is when Maggie starts fancyin' the same lad.

"A Guid Baddie"
Basil Rathbone fought with Robin Hood in "The Adventures Of Robin Hood" and Moriarty in "Sherlock Holmes And The Secret Weapon". He couldnae get on wi' onybody.

"Busy-Busy? Beehave Yourself!"
"Charley's Big-Hearted Aunt" starred Arthur Askey — no' awfy tall, but never short on laughs!

FOR THE LADDIES

"The Bee's Knees Wi' A Chimp In The Trees"
Johnny Weissmuller as Tarzan. Whit a life — nae baths — just a dook in the burn when ye had tae fecht a crocodile or somethin'!

"Scary Or Whit?"
Lon Chaney Jnr was greetin' — a' the way tae the bank after starring in "The Ghost Of Frankenstein" and "Frankenstein Meets The Wolfman".

"On The Fiddle"
Haud on tae yer sweetie coupons.
Here's Jack Benny who starred in "The Meanest Man In The World".

"Play It Again, Wullie"
Here's Humphrey Bogart, who starred in "The Maltese Falcon" and "Casablanca". Watch oot for the Bogieman!

OOR WULLIE 1940-1949

The Sunday Post 13th June 1943

The Sunday Post 11th July 1943

OOR WULLIE 1940-1949

The Sunday Post 18th July 1943

The Sunday Post 12th September 1943

The Sunday Post 26th September 1943

The Sunday Post 19th September 1943

The Sunday Post 10th October 1943

OOR WULLIE 1940-1949

The Sunday Post 31st October 1943

OOR WULLIE 1940-1949

The Sunday Post 5th March 1944

The Sunday Post 7th November 1943

The Sunday Post 23rd April 1944

The Sunday Post 21st November 1943

OOR WULLIE 1940-1949

The Sunday Post 14th May 1944

The Sunday Post 30th April 1944

The Sunday Post 7th May 1944

OOR WULLIE 1940-1949

The Sunday Post 11th June 1944

The Sunday Post 21st May 1944

The Sunday Post 16th July 1944

The Sunday Post 4th June 1944

" We are now in the third year of peace . . . "

CARTOON CAPERS

The Broons and Oor Wullie didn't have a monopoly on fun. Here are a selection of cartoons which were printed and enjoyed in The Sunday Post during The Roaring Forties.

" She's been wearin' thae claes for 40 years, an' she's in the fashion at last ! "

" Ah must get wan o' thae coats wi' the sleeves ye don't pit yer airms in ! "

" Gie me a shout when the fitba' season starts ! "

" It's a wee bit o' consolation for him since he had tae lay up the car."

" Coupon free, tae ! "

OOR WULLIE 1940-1949

The Sunday Post 13th August 1944

The Sunday Post 2nd July 1944

The Sunday Post 30th July 1944

The Sunday Post 11th February 1945

The Sunday Post 3rd December 1944

OOR WULLIE 1940-1949

The Sunday Post 14th January 1945

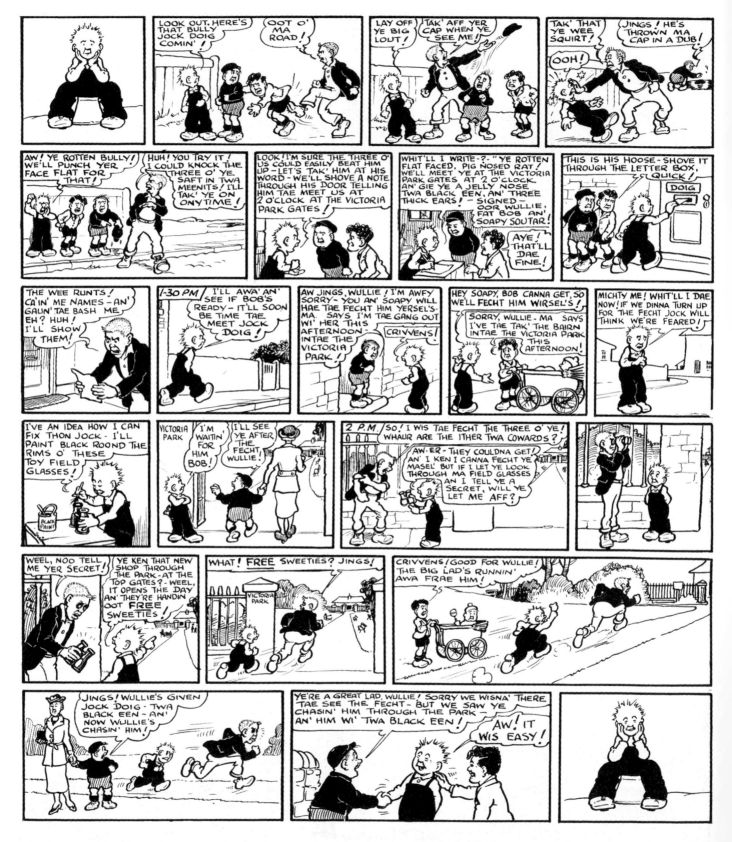

The Sunday Post 18th February 1945

The Sunday Post 22nd April 1945

The Sunday Post 25th February 1945

OOR WULLIE 1940-1949

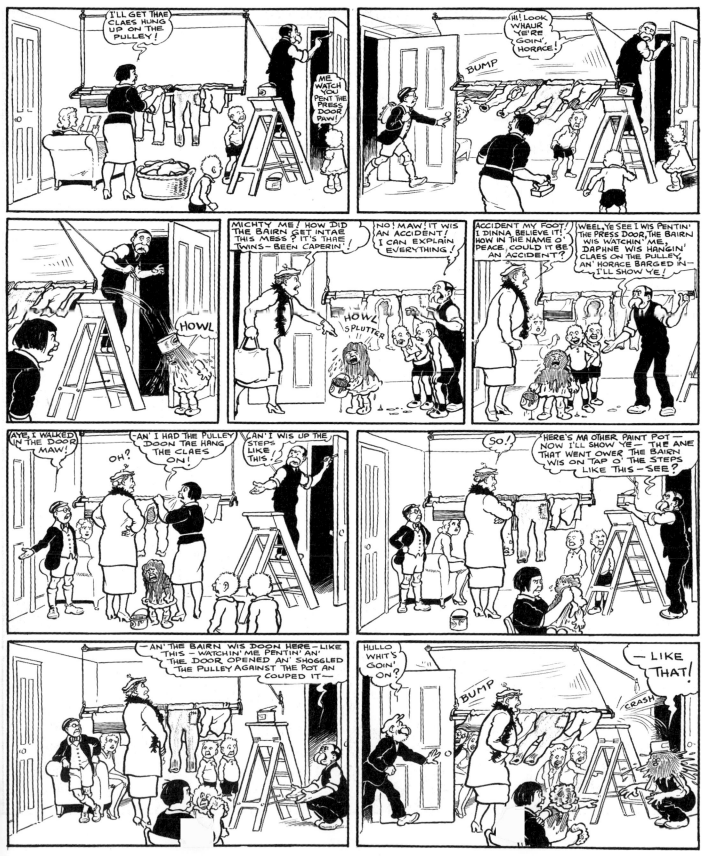

The Sunday Post 17th June 1945

The Sunday Post 22nd July 1945

OOR WULLIE 1940-1949

The Sunday Post 9th December 1945

The Sunday Post 13th January 1946

The Sunday Post 7th April 1946

The Sunday Post 20th January 1946

A NICHT AT THE PICTERS

"The Bad Lad" Richard Widmark played a really vile villain in "Kiss Of Death". Maw Broon couldnae believe it an' said, "He looks like marge wouldnae melt in his mooth."

"Okaye-dokaye" Danny Kaye had a secret life — he wis Walter Mitty tae. Can ye imagine it? Danny could.

"On Her Taes" Speakin' o' dancers, here's another — it's Moira Shearer, star o' "The Red Shoes". The Bairn Broon wondered why she didnae wear high heels instead o' standin' on tippy-taes.

"A Chip Aff The Auld Bloke" Cornel Wilde is Robin Hood's youngster in "The Bandit Of Sherwood Forest". He's a' grown-up noo' an' can dae feats o' derring-do instead of derring-dinnae dae that"

FOR THE LADIES

"Oor Williams" Esther Williams was a real bathing beauty in "Bathing Beauty" — a picter fair fu o' sweemin' weemin!

"Anybody Here Seen Kelly" "Aye — I've seen Gene — in 'Cover Girl' an' in ma dreams." Hands up wha guessed it wis Daphne speakin'.

"Tell It Tae The Marines" United States Marine Sergeant Glenn Ford married Eleanor Powell, but it didnae stop him cleanin' up the toon in "The Desperadoes".

"Dinnae Ca' Me A Jesse — I'm Frank." Henry was Fonda nothin' better than laughin' a' the way tae the bank — then robbin' it, in "Jesse James".

"Gregory's Grill" Gregory Peck did — in "Duel In The Sun" — withoot ony suntan lotion.

"Smile When You Say That! " A famous line from the original 1929 version of "The Virginian". Joel McCrea starred in the 1946 remake.

"No' Sae Bad Sinbad " Douglas Fairbanks Junior in "Sinbad The Sailor". Paw Broon kens a' aboot their magic carpet — when Maw tells him tae beat it he vanishes for oors!

"Help Ma Bob" Robert Mitchum didnae need onybody's help in films like "Blood On The Moon" and "Nevada".

The Sunday Post 3rd March 1946

The Sunday Post 28th April 1946

The Sunday Post 10th March 1946

OOR WULLIE 1940-1949

The Sunday Post 14th July 1946

The Sunday Post 7th April 1946

OOR WULLIE 1940-1949

Certain gags wouldn't appear in these p.c. days.

The Sunday Post 27th October 1946

The Sunday Post 16th June 1946

The Sunday Post 11th August 1946

OOR WULLIE 1940-1949

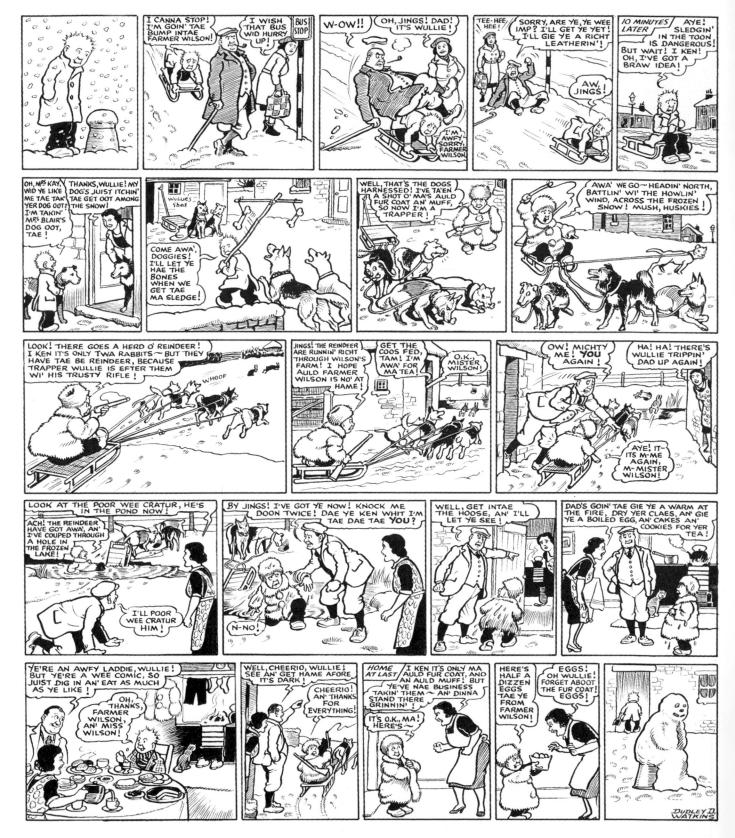

The Sunday Post 12th January 1947

The Sunday Post 20th April 1947

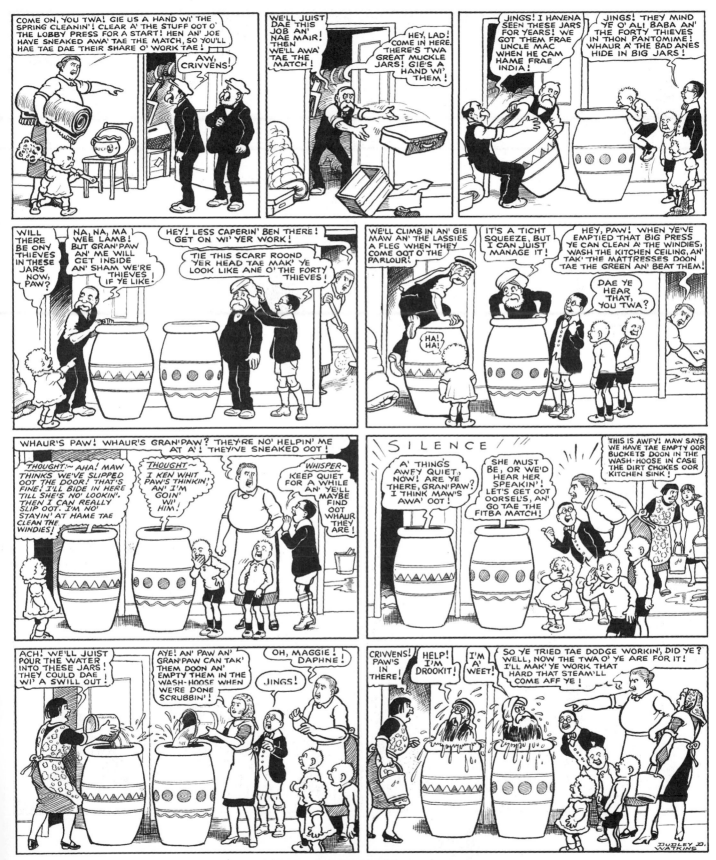

The Sunday Post 27th April 1947

OOR WULLIE 1940-1949

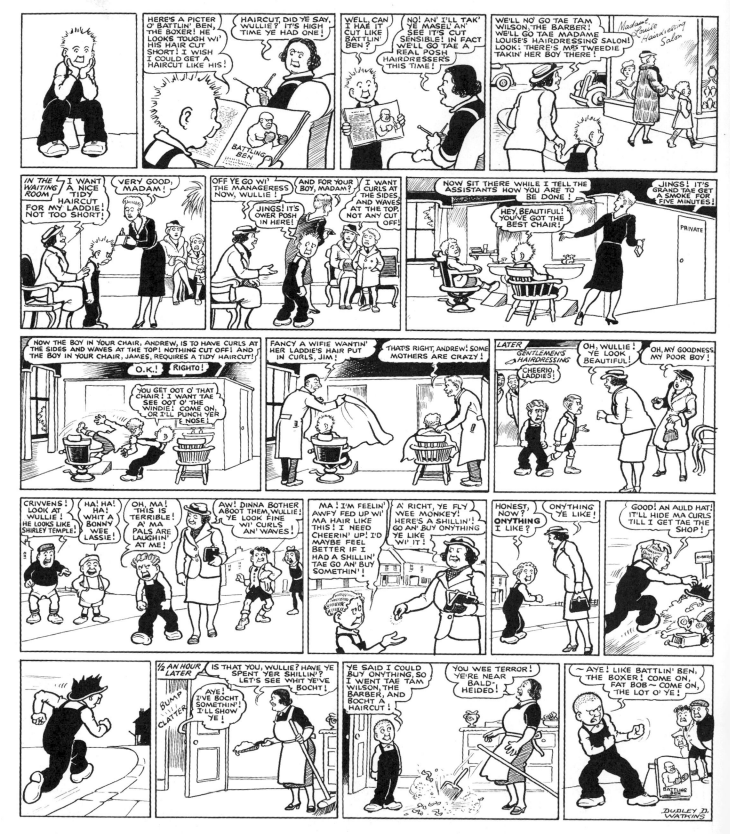

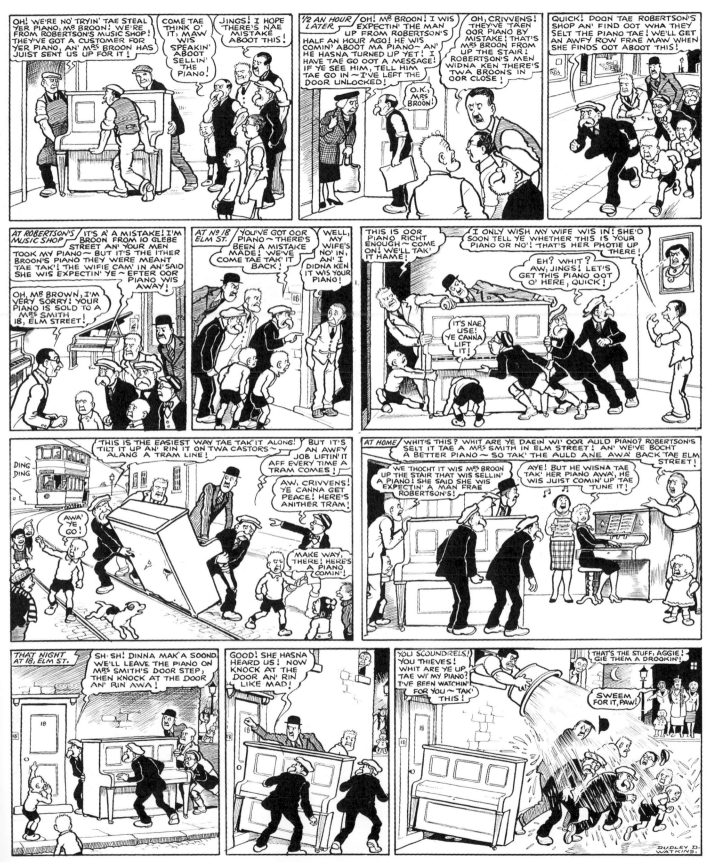

The Sunday Post 4th May 1947

OOR WULLIE 1940-1949

The Sunday Post 8th June 1947

OOR WULLIE 1940-1949

The Sunday Post 13th July 1947

The Sunday Post 13th July 1947

The Sunday Post 20th July 1947

OOR WULLIE 1940-1949

The Sunday Post 18th January 1948

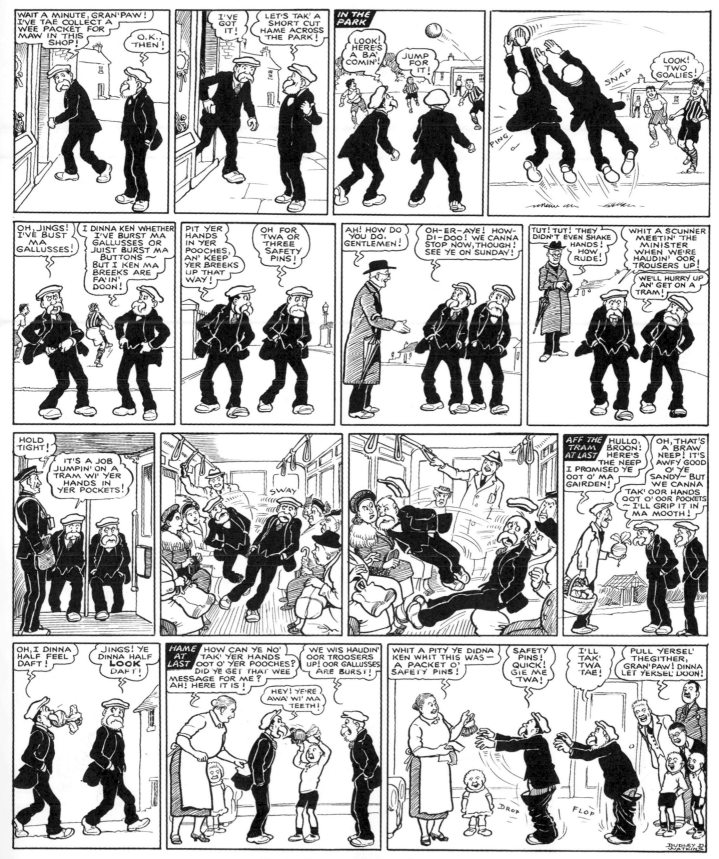

The Sunday Post 7th December 1947

A Rangers Fan Tells What It Costs

WILLIAM ANDERSON, a docker, of 10 Gower Street, Ibrox, is a member of Rangers Supporters' Club. Everywhere the Light Blues go, he follows.

What does this hobby cost?

Yesterday Bill made the long journey to Aberdeen. Cost—£2. Earlier in the season a trip to Dundee knocked him back £1 1s 6d. Same for the Dumfries trip.

When Rangers scraped through the cup-tie at Stranraer, he paid £1 12s 6d to see them do it.

Bill's outlay for the season is £15. It would be a lot more if he wasn't a member of the Supporters' Club. Buses for away games are hired on a non-profit-making basis.

£15 may seem a lot of money. "But it's worth it," says Bill.

WHIT'S IN THE SUNDAY POST TODAY?

Apart frae fish an' chips, here's a wee selection o' some o' he best an' funniest things tae appear in the late 40s.

THE MINISTER AND "OOR WULLIE"

"BEAR ye one another's burdens—just like Oor Wullie in ' The Sunday Post,'" said Rev. Charles Gibson, M.A., in his children's address at Knox's Church, Arbroath, last Sunday.

"Wullie's the kind of chap who keeps on trying," Mr Gibson told the children.

"Far too many people don't try to help. Or they give up too soon because they think it can't be done. That's the wrong way to go through life.

"If you read ' Oor Wullie,' you'll discover he's the sort of chap who tries a thing first. He tries pleasantly and willingly. If his good deed is successful, so much to the good. If he's unsuccessful, at least he's tried.

"That's the great thing.

"Why not take a leaf out of Wullie's book?" Mr Gibson asked the children.

"If you make a mistake, people will sympathise. But they will not be pleased if you never even try."

Every Sunday Mr Gibson gives a short address for the children. His text is based on something familiar to them all. Last week's theme was Wullie's efforts to repay Fat Bob's uncle for the week-end Wullie had in the country.

Now Here's A New Hair-Do For Men

THE " Crew Haircut " has come to Scotland. Young men are asking specially for it.

The " Crew cut " originated in the U.S. Army and is now the rage at universities. The hair is cut close all over the head except the top. From crown to forehead it's left about two inches long, so that it sticks straight up like a brush.

American students like it because wearing football helmets, close-fitting caps, &c., is made easier. It keeps the hair from falling into their eyes during play.

Barbers say it's the coolest and cleanest way to wear hair during summer. The cropping helps growth And the hair never needs to be combed.

The Moment the Whole Train Waited For

AT first I couldn't understand it. As the express for Dublin sped south, the passengers grew restive. They peered at watches. They looked anxiously through the windows for landmarks. They loitered round the deserted bar close by the dining-car.

" What are they all so anxious about?" I asked the bar-tender.

" Just wait till we get over the Border," he grinned. Then I noticed the price-list:—

	Ulster Price.	Free State.
Whisky	2s 6d	1s 4d
Bottled Beer	1s 4d	8d

Suddenly a bell trilled. " We're across!" said the barman, and pushed back his cuffs.

I was almost forced under the counter by the rush. The place was like a beehive. Waiters wilted. Corks popped. We were in the Free State, drinking tax-free—at 70 miles an hour!—D. D.

Holiday Digs To Be Dearer

HOLIDAY digs will be dearer this summer.

For a man, wife, and two children, the bill for a week will, many cases, be up by at least 30s—£1 more for parents and ha price for the bairns.

More digs will be in the £4 a week class.

Some small hotels will increase top prices from 6 to 6½ g Larger hotels and boarding-houses will charge up to 21s a week mo

A Dunoon boarding-house is charging £4 18s per week for Ju September—compared with £4 7s 6d last season.

Average price in Largs is 15s a day. In some cases this is increase from 12s 6d, 13s, or 14s.

An Aberdeen boarding-house charge for full board is up fr £4 7s 6d to £5 5s.

Channel Tunnel In 9 Years: New British-French Plan

MUSIC WHILE YOU WALK

MR HARRY E. FAIRLEY, of Edinburgh, has just bought what he believes to be the cutest radio in the country.

It weighs under 2 lb., is 9 in. long, 5½ in. deep, 2 in. thick.

It's carried over the shoulder like a lady's shoulder-bag. The aerial is inside the plastic strap.

There was only one of its kind in the London shop where Mr Fairley bought it. It cost £21.

He immediately tried it out in Oxford Street. It caused a mild sensation. Everybody gave him a look of astonishment when they heard the radio going as he passed.

Few spotted the gadget slung over his shoulder.

So, if you hear music coming from "nowhere" in an Edinburgh street, look for Mr Fairley!

£50 MILLION COST

Plans for a tunnel running under the Straits of Dover to Fance were discussed by British and French engineers and M.P.s yesterday.

Cost will be between £40 million and £50 million.

The project may be realised in eight or nine years, if the two Governments accept their representatives' recommendations.

Lieutenant-Commander Powell, spokesman for the British delegation, said labour costs would be light.

About 250 British and French workers will be employed directly and about 750 from both countries indirectly.

The meeting, which was held in Paris, agreed to form a joint committee from members of upper and lower Houses of Parliament in both countries to study the project.

British and French plans at present differ in some respects.

DICK BARTON IRE IN DUMBARTONSHIRE

DUMBARTONSHIRE police, called to intervene in a domestic dispute, learned "Dick Barton" was the cause of all the trouble.

The husband was keen to listen to the exploits of the B.B.C. special agent and the wife had expressed a desire for a spot of music. Before the police arrived the husband had heard Barton through.

JUST THE THING FOR THE WIFE

The umbrella—full length.   Half-collapsed before folding.   Folded and ready for handbag.

I RECEIVED a parcel last week from a friend in Italy.

The Customs label on the outside said it contained an umbrella. That didn't seem possible, for the parcel was less than a foot long.

But it was an umbrella—and a full-length one at that. Its secret is that it folds in two.

I carry it around in my handbag. When rain comes on, I take it out, pull out the handle and straighten the ribs. It's a beautifully finished job, and looks just like any other umbrella.

When the rain goes off, I fold it up, fasten on a separate matching cover so that it won't soak everything in my bag, and stow it away again.

The umbrella is popular in Italy and America, and is now coming on to the British market in very small numbers at £4 10s.—Priscilla.

OPERATION HAMPDEN

The laurel leaf for enterprise surely goes to the soldier who managed to get into Hampden WITHOUT A TICKET!

One moment he was a disconsolate H.L.I. private waiting outside the ground. The next he filled a convenient blank file in the rear of an incoming Army cadet company. He marched through the gate with a surprised cadet at each elbow.

WEE ORGAN BEAT THE BIG YIN!

NEW YEAR reveller in a Glasgow cinema raised a laugh from the audience during an organ interlude. He produced a mouth organ from his pocket and made the solo a duet.

His spasmodic "toot-toot" brought a new note of merriment to a Viennese waltz. It went down well with the crowd.

Naturally the organist didn't appreciate the voluntary. He threw in the towel halfway through the fight!

OOR WULLIE 1940-1949

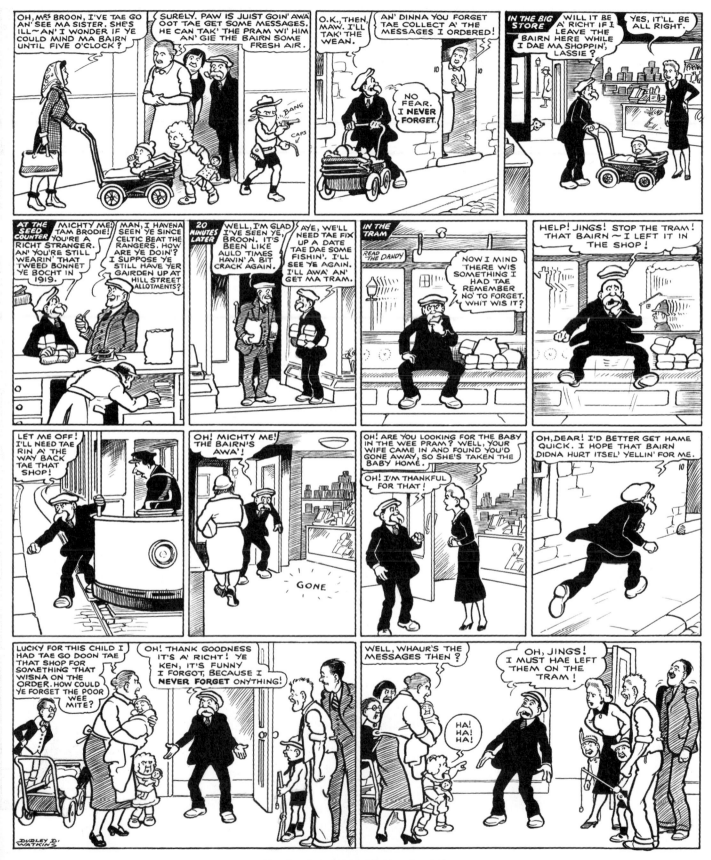

The Sunday Post 14th March 1948

OOR WULLIE 1940-1949

The Sunday Post 18th April 1948

The Sunday Post 22nd February 1948

The Sunday Post 25th April 1948

OOR WULLIE 1940-1949

The Sunday Post 9th May 1948

The Sunday Post 6th June 1948

OOR WULLIE 1940-1949

ISBN 0-85116-804-3
Printed and published in Great Britain by D.C. Thomson & Co., Ltd., 185 Fleet Street, London EC4A 2HS. © D.C. Thomson & Co., Ltd., 2002

The Sunday Post 27th March 1949

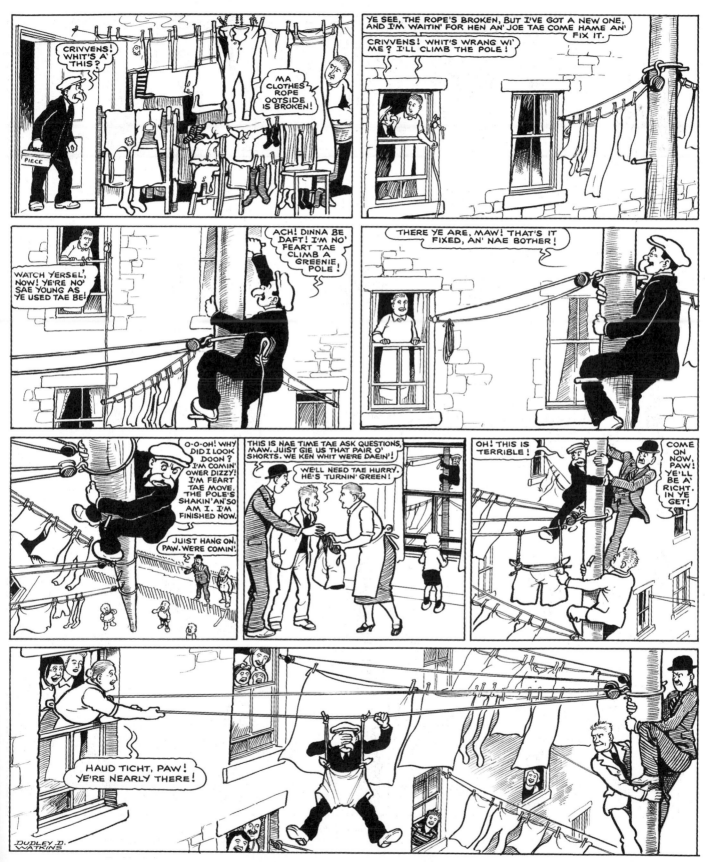

The Sunday Post 13th June 1948